Gerald
Finzi

Prelude
from *Requiem da Camera*

arranged by Howard Ferguson

Piano Duet

BOOSEY & HAWKES

Boosey & Hawkes Music Publishers Ltd
www.boosey.com

Published by Boosey & Hawkes Music Publishers Ltd
Aldwych House
71–91 Aldwych
London
WC2B 4HN

www.boosey.com

© Copyright 2013 by Boosey & Hawkes Music Publishers Ltd
This arrangement © copyright 2014 by Boosey & Hawkes Music Publishers Ltd

ISMN 979-0-060-12912-4
ISBN 978-1-78454-002-9

This impression 2014

Printed in the EU by Halstan

Music origination by New Notations London

PUBLISHER'S NOTE

Gerald Finzi's *Requiem da Camera*, scored for baritone, mixed chorus (or SATB soli) and small orchestra, was his first attempt at composing an extended work comprising several movements. Dating from 1923–24, the wellspring of its composition was the death, during active service in 1918, of his first composition teacher, Ernest Farrar.

The *Requiem* comprises four movements: an instrumental prelude and settings of verses from John Masefield's *August, 1914*, of Thomas Hardy's *In Time of 'The Breaking of Nations'* and of W W Gibson's 'Lament', from *Whin*. During the 1930s Finzi decided to write an entirely new version of the Hardy setting but this was only partially completed. At the request of the Finzi Trust a new edition (with completion) was made by Christian Alexander, which was first performed in 2013.

The Prelude was the only part of the *Requiem da Camera* to be performed during Finzi's lifetime, played by the London Chamber Orchestra, conducted by Anthony Bernard, on 1 December 1925 at Court House, Marylebone Lane, London, under the auspices of the British Music Society.

The piano duet arrangement of the Prelude by Finzi's friend and collaborator Howard Ferguson forms part of the manuscript vocal score of the *Requiem* and is dated 1924.

February 2014

Duration: 6 minutes

Requiem da Camera

Study score and vocal score on sale
Orchestral materials available on hire
Organ reduction by Francis Jackson on sale

PRELUDE

from Requiem da Camera

Arrangement for piano duet by
HOWARD FERGUSON
(1908–99)

GERALD FINZI
(1901–56)

19459

Appassionato

Appassionato

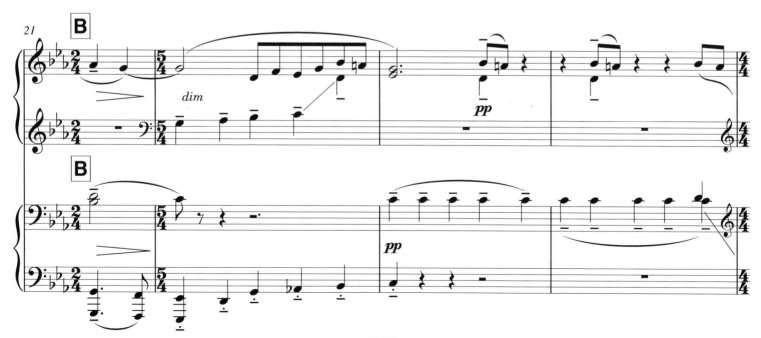

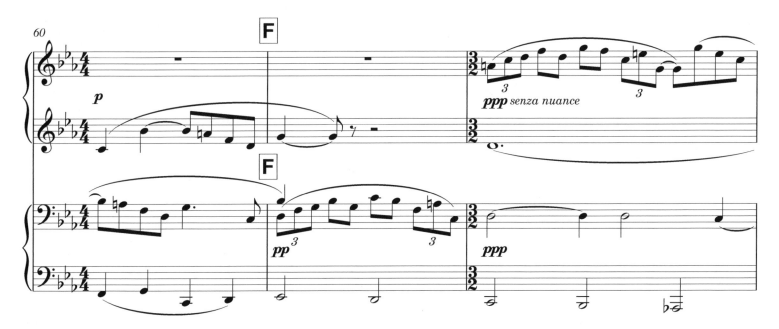

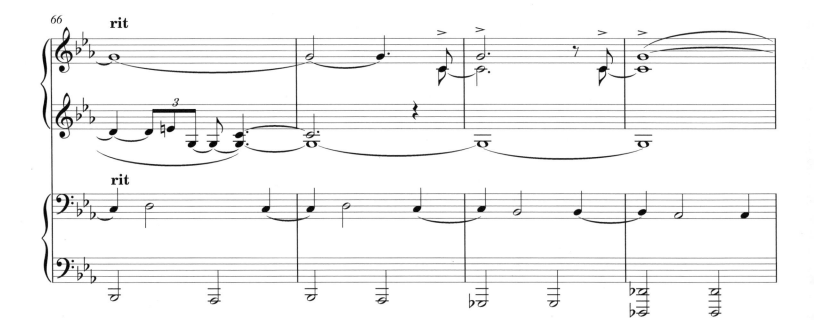

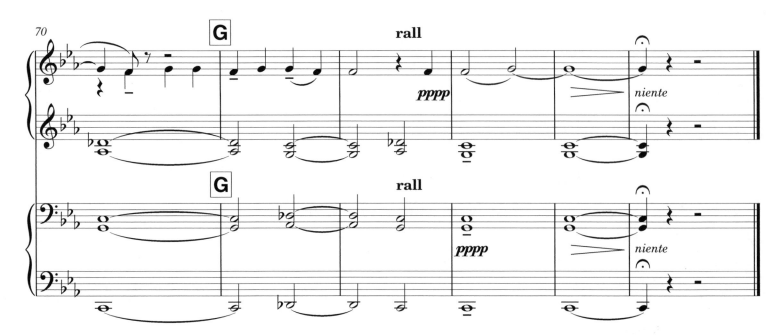

Music for
Two Pianos

Original works and arrangements

Adams
Hallelujah Junction

Andriessen
Séries

Argento
Valentino Dances

Bartók
Seven Pieces from Mikrokosmos
Sonata for Two Pianos and Percussion
Suite, op 4b

Bernstein, arr Musto
Symphonic Dances from West Side Story

Britten
Introduction and Rondo alla Burlesca, op 23 no 1
Mazurka Elegiaca, op 23 no 2
Scottish Ballad, op 26
2 pianos and orchestra

Copland
Billy the Kid (excerpts from the ballet)
Dance of the Adolescent from Dance Symphony
Danza de Jalisco
Danzón Cubano
Hoe Down and Saturday Night Waltz from Rodeo
El Salón México

Delius, arr Balfour Gardiner
Poem of Life and Love

Einem
Arietten, op 50

Ferguson
Partita

Gerhard
Alegrías
Pandora Suite
2 pianos and percussion

Glanert
Enigmatische Landschaft
Tanzende Landschaft

Höller
Diaphonie
Partita

Holloway
Gilded Goldbergs

Markevitch
L'Envol d'Icare
2 pianos and percussion

Maxwell Davies
Four Lessons for Two Keyboards

Rachmaninoff
Fantaisie (Suite no 1), op 5
Suite no 2, op 17
Symphonic Dances, op 45

Rorem
Six Variations

Shostakovich
Suite
Tarantella

Stravinsky
Madrid
Pétrouchka
Septet
Three Movements from Pétrouchka (arr Babin)

BOOSEY & HAWKES

AN IMAGEM COMPANY

Ad 401